Reprinted in 2017

An imprint of Om Books International

Corporate & Editorial Office
A 12, Sector 64, Noida 201 301
Uttar Pradesh, India
Phone: +91 120 477 4100
Email: editorial@ombooks.com
Website: www.ombooksinternational.com

Sales Office
107, Ansari Road, Darya Ganj
New Delhi 110 002, India
Phone: +91 11 4000 9000
Fax: +91 11 2327 8091
Email: sales@ombooks.com
Website: www.ombooks.com

ISBN : 978-93-80070-13-1

Printed in India

10 9 8 7 6 5 4

HANUMAN

The Mighty God

An imprint of Om Books International

High up in Heaven, Lord Brahma was meditating on his lotus throne. When he opened his eyes, he saw a heavenly maiden weeping. Brahma called out to the maiden and asked, "My dear child, What is the cause of your sorrow?"

The maiden replied, "Lord Brahma, I am under a terrible curse." When Brahma asked her what it was, she said, "Some time ago, I went to Earth to see what it was like. There I saw a strange sight. A monkey sat deep in meditation.

I poked fun of him and so threw stones at him. Alas! That was a sage in the form of a monkey. I had unknowingly disturbed him. He opened his eyes in anger and cursed me

that I would turn into a monkey the day I fell in love. "Oh Lord! Can you rid me of this curse? pleaded the maiden." Lord Brahma fell into deep thought as he could not rid her of the curse completely. "There is a way out of the curse, but you have to be patient," said Brahma.

"Your curse will end as soon as you give birth to an incarnation of Lord Shiva! Pray to him. The time has come for you to leave Heaven and live on Earth."

And that is how Anjana, the mother of Hanuman, came to Earth. She lived in a forest. One day while wandering in the forest, she saw a strong man fighting with a lion. She fell in

love the moment she saw him, and could feel her face changing into that of a monkey. "The curse is taking effect!" panicked Anjana. She let out a scream and fell to the ground. The man rushed to her thinking he had scared her.

Anjana was too scared to show him her face, and so she just peeped through the gaps of her fingers to see what he was like. And she was in for a happy surprise! "He has a monkey's face too!" thought Anjana. "I am Kesari, the king of monkeys," said the young man. "Oh lovely maiden! Will you marry me?" Anjana was still in shock. But she agreed right away. Kesari and Anjana married with the blessings of the elders.

The time when Anjana and Kesari lived in the forest, in another part of the world, King Dasharatha—the ruler of Ayodhya— was performing a holy sacrifice to have children. Agni, the God of Fire, came out of the holy fire with a bowl filled with a sweet for the three queens of Dasharatha. "Dasharatha, give your three queens a portion of this sweet and you

will soon be blessed with strong and intelligent sons," said Agni. Dasharatha obeyed Agni and gave the sweet to his queens. When he had finished giving the sweet to his third wife, a bird flew in suddenly. The bird snatched the bowl from Dasharatha's hands and flew up into the sky. The potion fell from the bird's claws and

was falling to the ground when Vayu, the Wind God blew the potion softly towards Anjana, who was worshipping in the forest.

Anjana was surprised to see the potion in her hands. She wondered, "What is this? It looks like a blessing from God himself." And so, she ate the sweet, thanking God. A few months later,

Anjana gave birth to a lovely baby, who was named Anjaneya—the son of Anjana.

Anjaneya grew up to be a chubby child. He would always be found smiling. But Anjaneya was restless like all children. One

day, he was very hungry and looked around everywhere for his mother. "Mother! I am hungry!" shouted Anjaneya. But Anjana was not to be found anywhere. Anjaneya was standing by the window at that time. He looked out of the window and up in the sky he saw something that looked a red apple. "Oh! That looks delicious," thought Anjaneya. "There is a red apple waiting to be

plucked. I will go and get it." And with that, he leapt into the sky. What he did not know was that the red apple was actually the Sun!

Anjaneya flew like the wind into the skies. Right at the time when he was flying to get the

Sun, Rahu—the Snake God—was going to cover the Sun God. Anjaneya caught Rahu and refused to leave him for some time. Rahu was almost choked with Anjaneya's tight clasp, when he was suddenly released. Frightened, Rahu ran to

Indra, the king of all the gods. "Indra, I have just survived from the clutches of a child with a monkey face. Though he was a child, he held me with a mighty force. Who is he?" asked Rahu.

Indra smiled and replied, "He is Anjaneya, the son of Anjana and Kesari." Meanwhile, the Sun God asked his charioteer, "Who is that little boy coming towards us with such speed?" When the charioteer told him that it was Anjaneya and he was coming to get them, the Sun God ran to Indra. "Save me, Indra! Save me from the mighty Anjaneya."

Indra took his chariot and rode towards Anjaneya. "The ripe fruit you are flying towards is the Sun God, my child! Leave him alone," said Indra. But Anjaneya was adamant. He refused

to listen. Indra thought to himself, "How do I stop him? He will not listen and I cannot let the Sun be captured by him. The world will suffer!" Finally, Indra picked up Vajra, his weapon, and flung it at Anjaneya to stop him from flying ahead. Indra's weapon was a very powerful one and Anjaneya came tumbling down to Earth within seconds. He lay on the grass unconscious. Vayu, the Wind God, saw this and ran to Anjaneya's help. Seeing him speechless and unconscious, Vayu was angry with all the gods for hurting

such a young child. "As this child suffers, let the world suffer! I will take back all the air from this Earth and go away," cried out Vayu. He took Anjaneya and went deep into the chambers of Mother Earth.

All the three worlds were now without air. People could not breathe and were choked. There was panic everywhere. Finally, everyone ran to Indra, pleading him to save them. "Save us from this hell, or soon we will all die!" cried the gods. The Sun God cursed himself for what had happened. "It was me who ran for help to Indra," said the Sun God to Lord Brahma. Brahma heard everyone's pleas and told Indra, "You must apologise to Vayu. Beg him to

come back or soon everything will perish."Indra immediately rode to where Vayu was and said, "Vayu, please accept my apologies and return." Both Brahma and Indra blessed Hanuman with great powers. "You took the force of my weapon

on your cheeks (Hanu in Sanskrit) and will be known from now on as the great Hanuman."

Anjaneya grew up to be a very curious child. He would peep into the nests of birds to see their little children. "Look how cute these fledglings are," Anjaneya would say, looking at the nest of birds.

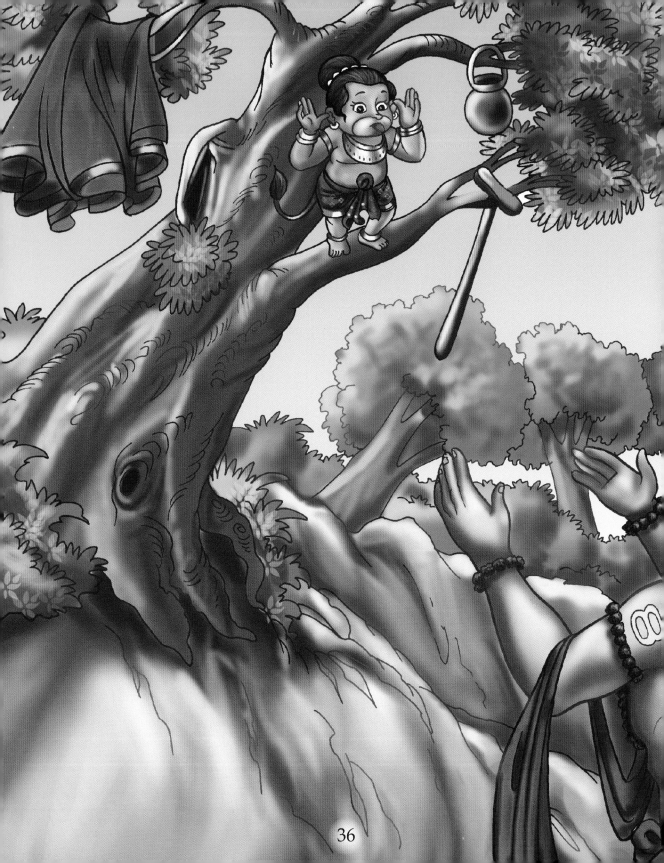

He would run around forests with his other friends. Anjaneya was fearless, but was very naughty. He would often trouble the sages living in the forests. "Look! Little Anjaneya took my sacred pot away," said one sage. "Oh! He always takes my sacred beads away," said another. "We

have to stop this little child from wrecking our lives," said another sage. But Anjaneya was always as swift as the wind.

One day, Anjaneya was being his naughty self, and ran away with a basket of flowers a

sage had collected for his prayers. The sage cursed Anjaneya, "You will forget all the powers you have."

Anjaneya could not believe his ears. "What will I tell my parents now!" trembled the little one. He begged the sage for forgiveness with tears in his eyes. The sage was moved and decided to find a way, as a curse once given can never be taken back. "You will remember your powers at the right time, when someone reminds you of them," said the sage.

Hanuman grew up to be handsome and strong. He was the Minister in the court of Sugreev, the king of monkeys. Sugreev's brother, Bali, had banished him from the kingdom. So,

Sugreev with his trusted followers, was living in the forest.

Far away in Ayodhya, Rama was sent to exile for fourteen years. He had come to live in the forest with brother Lakshmana and wife Sita. But evil Ravana

had kidnapped Sita.Rama and Lakshmana had set out to find her. News reached the ears of Sugreev that two young men were entering their part of the forest. Sugreev was anxious. "Could these men have been sent by my brother Bali?"

he wondered. He called Hanuman and said, "Hanuman! You are the only one who can find out who these men are and tell me whether they are friends or foes." Hanuman set out to meet Rama and Lakshmana, disguised as an old man.

44

"What are you looking for?" asked Hanuman when he spotted Rama and Lakshmana.

"We are Rama and Lakshmana, princes of Ayodhya. My wife has been kidnapped by Ravana. We are on a mission to rescue her," said Rama.

"Then come with me," said Hanuman assuming his real form. He took them to Sugreev and told him all about them and Sita. Sugreev promised to help Rama, but also asked for his help in getting back his kingdom and family.

Rama helped Sugreev in defeating Bali, and crowned him King. Within a few days, Sugreev sent out small teams in different directions to find Sita. Hanuman, Jambavan—the Bear King—

and a team of monkeys went south. At the southern-most tip was only the sea. "What will we do now? We don't know whether Sita was taken beyond the sea!" said one monkey.

"I know where she was taken," said an old voice. Everyone turned to find an old vulture walking towards them. "I am Sampati, the brother of Jatayu," said the bird.

"Your brave brother was killed by the evil Ravana, while he was trying to rescue Sita," said Jambavan. Sampati vowed to avenge his brother's death. He told them Ravana lived in Lanka, across the sea with his evil forces.

"But who will go across the sea?" thought Jambavan. Then he looked at Hanuman. "If there is anyone among us who has the power to cross

the sea, it is you!" said Jambavan to Hanuman. "Me? How can I cross such a big sea?" asked Hanuman. "You have great powers waiting to be remembered! Think of Lord Rama and you will get your powers back," said Jambavan. Hanuman stood on top of a rock and meditated upon Lord Rama. Slowly he started growing in size. The monkeys watched Hanuman grow as high as the sky!

Then he took one giant leap and flew across the sea. When he had flown a few miles,

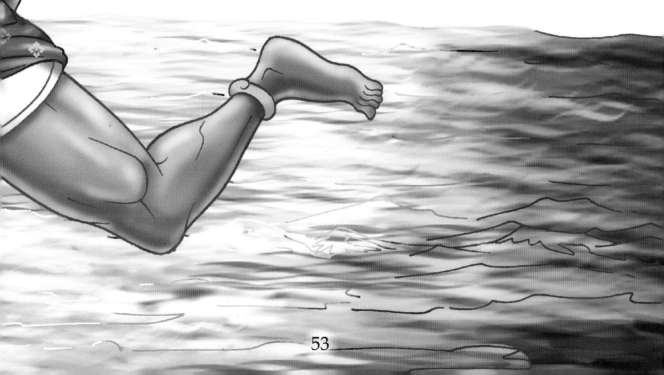

Hanuman suddenly hit a giant mountain, which had emerged from the waters, with his chest. "I am Mainaka! Your father had helped me once. I would like to repay that help by offering you a place to rest for a while on your long journey." "I do not have the time to rest," said Hanuman and flew ahead. A little ahead, Hanuman saw a huge demoness come out of the waters. It was Sinhika. "You have to enter my mouth, if you have to go ahead," said Sinhika. "So be it!" said Hanuman, and suddenly shrunk himself as

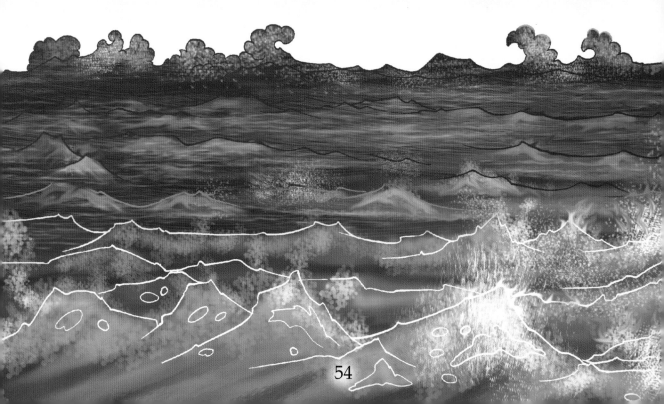

small as a fly, and swiftly flew in and out of Sinhika's demonic mouth.

Then, Surasa, a demon in the form of a huge snake came out of the waters. She swallowed Hanuman. Hanuman tore her stomach and came out of

it within minutes. He continued his flight till he reached the gates of Lanka at night. Hanuman saw a demoness guarding the gates. He walked towards the gates quietly, but the demoness heard his footsteps and said, "Stop!

Who goes there? You have to defeat Lankini to go ahead!" Hanuman defeated Lankini in a fight but did not kill her as she was a woman.

Then he entered Lanka and went from one place to the other till he finally reached Ravana's palace. He saw many beautiful women there but not Sita. After roaming around a little more, he reached the tree top of the garden where Ravana had kept Sita.

Hanuman saw Sita surrounded by demonesses. As he planned to approach her, he heard the sound of footsteps. He saw Ravana walking towards Sita. "Forget Rama and marry me, Sita! How long will you moan for your husband?" asked Ravana. "Go away, evil one. My lord will come one day to rescue me and punish you for all your evil deeds," cried Sita. Ravana went away in a

huff.

A little later, when all the demonesses had slept, Hanuman dropped Rama's ring in Sita's lap. "My Lord! He is here!" exclaimed Sita with joy. Hanuman slowly came down the tree and said, "Mother! Your worries are over. Lord Rama is on his way here and will defeat the evil Ravana and take you home."

Then Hanuman fought a few of the demons guarding the garden and

allowed himself to be captured, so as to get a chance to be taken before Ravana. When Ravana did not offer a seat to him, Hanuman created one by growing his tail and swirling it in circles to create a throne higher than that of Ravana.

"Who are you, monkey?" asked Ravana angrily. "I am Lord Rama's humble servant. If you don't release Sita immediately, you and your kingdom will have to pay a heavy price," said Hanuman. "Take him away and set fire to his tail," ordered

Ravana. But clever Hanuman set fire to all of Lanka by jumping from one house to the other. After causing enough damage to Lanka, he flew back to Lord Rama. "I found Sita!" he said and told Rama about the sad condition

in which Sita lived.

Rama's army built a bridge of stones over the sea with the help of the Sea God and marched into Lanka. A fierce battle took place between both sides. Indrajit, the son of Ravana, injured Lakshmana severely. Lakshmana was unconscious and only the Sanjeevani herb from a mountain in the Himalayas could save him. But that had to be brought back before

dawn the next day. Hanuman saw Rama's plight and took off for the Himalayas. When he reached the Himalayas, Hanuman was wonderstruck. "I was told that Sanjeevani would twinkle in the dark. But all these other herbs are also twinkling. Which one do I carry?" wondered Hanuman. With no time to waste,

he uprooted the entire mountain and carried it on his palm back to Lanka. Thus, Hanuman saved Lakshmana's life with his strength and special powers.

Rama finally killed Ravana in

the battle and rescued Sita.

He crowned Vibhishan, Ravana's brother as the next king of Lanka. Rama, Lakshmana and Sita flew back with Hanuman and Sugreev to Ayodhya. After Rama was crowned as the King of Ayodhya, he decided to give gifts to everyone

who had helped him in rescuing Sita. When it came to Hanuman, Sita stepped forward and gave her special pearl necklace to Hanuman.

But he pulled out each pearl and inspected it. All the courtiers were shocked to see Hanuman disrespecting Sita's gift. But Hanuman said, "I was only seeing whether my Lord Rama was there in these pearls. Otherwise, this necklace

has no meaning for me."

When one morning Hanuman saw Sita putting sindur (vermilion) on her forehead, he asked her the reason for it. "It is for the good health of Lord Rama," replied Sita. From that day on, Hanuman applied sindur to his

entire body.

While in court with Rama and Sita one day, Hanuman heard one of the courtiers whispering, "Why is Lord Rama so partial to Hanuman? He has so many more devotees." Hanuman tore his chest in answer to this, and everyone was surprised to see Lord Rama and Sita in Hanuman's heart! Hanuman's devotion to Rama was

beyond anyone's imagination.

It is said, to this day, that when one says the word Rama in prayer, Hanuman appears in an invisible form and stays on to listen to his Lord's prayer.

Brave Hanuman will remain in our prayers as the greatest example of strength, devotion, loyalty and humility.

OTHER TITLES IN THIS SERIES

     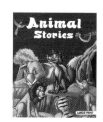

   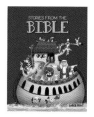  

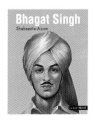 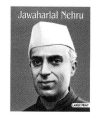 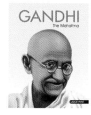   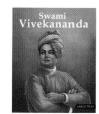

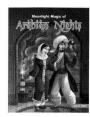 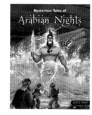   

OTHER TITLES IN THIS SERIES

   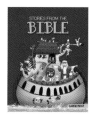  

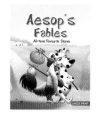 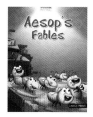    

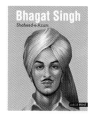 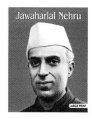 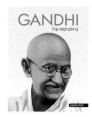   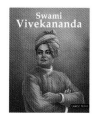

 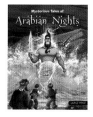  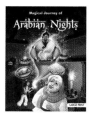